Inference
Reading Comprehension Book
Reading Level 3.5–5.0

––––––––––– **Introduction** –––––––––––

Welcome to the Edupress Inference Reading Comprehension Book. This resource is an effective tool for instruction, practice, and evaluation of student understanding of how to make inferences. It includes ideas on how to introduce inferring to students, as well as activities to help teach and practice the concept.

The reproducible activities in this book are tailored to individual, small-group, and whole-class work. They include leveled reading passages, graphic organizers, worksheets, and detailed instruction pages. These activities provide opportunities to use text, illustrations, graphics, and combinations of these elements to practice making inferences from text.

The material in this book is written for readers at the 3.5–5.0 reading level. However, the activities can easily be adapted to your students' ability levels and your time frame. After introducing an activity to students, model it by working through one or two examples aloud. You may wish to also read text passages aloud to students, or they can be read silently or aloud by students. For students who need personalized help, individual and small-group activities have been included. These activities can be done alone or with a classroom aide for explicit instruction.

We know you will be pleased with the progress your students make in being able to infer ideas from text after using this book.

EP2361 © 2010 Lab Safety Supply Inc. • 401 S. Wright Road • Janesville, WI 53547
ISBN 13: 978-1-56472-149-5
www.edupressinc.com

Table of Contents

Directions: Introducing Inference

Whole Class ● ● ●

Introduce the idea of using inference while reading. Think aloud, "If I'm inside with the shades drawn, and you all come into class wearing raincoats and carrying dripping umbrellas, I can infer it is raining outside. I'm not out in the rain, I don't see the rain, but I know people wear raincoats in the rain. I know umbrellas get wet in the rain. So I can put together what I see with what I know and infer that it is raining." Explain that good readers use this same process when they read. Explain that when readers make inferences, they take clues from the text and/or illustrations, add the clues to what they already know, and come up with ideas the author does not directly state. Read a short picture book, such as *The Relatives Came* by Cynthia Rylant. Show the class the book cover and read the title. Model making an inference, for example, "The title says the relatives came. In the picture, there are many suitcases on the roof of the car. I know I don't bring a suitcase for a day visit. I can take the fact from the picture and what I know and infer that the relatives are going for a long trip."

Read the first six pages of the story. Guide students in making an inference. Draw and label an inference graphic organizer on the board similar to the "Morning Chores" Graphic Organizer on page 5. Think aloud, "I wonder how the relatives feel?" Ask students what clues in the text and picture can help

them know this. Record their answers in the graphic organizer. Have students think about a time when they used the same actions. Ask how they felt at the time and record their answers in the organizer. Review the clues and the students' prior knowledge and ask, "How do the relatives feel?" Record the answer. Continue reading, pausing several times to guide students through making inferences.

Whole Class/Individual ● ● ● / ○

Reproduce "Morning Chores" on page 4 and the graphic organizer on page 5. Explain that sometimes readers only have clues from the text and what they already know to make inferences. Read the story aloud. Then, read the directions, questions, and labels on the graphic organizer aloud. Explain that the organizer will help the students make inferences to answer the questions. Reread the first question. Have students find clues in the text to help them fill in the first box. Then, have students record what they already know about the clues in the second box. Finally, instruct students to use what they wrote in the first two boxes to make an inference that answers the question and to write the answer in the third box. Have students continue the process independently until each question is completed.

When all students have finished, discuss the answers to the questions as a class. As an extension, ask students to explain how to make an inference in three simple steps.

Answer Key

"Morning Chores" Graphic Organizer (Page 6)

1. He still had a scar on his right hand from an unhappy hen pecking him last year. + prior knowledge will vary = Daniel is afraid of being hurt or pecked again by a hen.

2. I'll bring you to Aunt Nancy's chicken coop. You can gather the eggs, while I feed the pigs. Those are the cornfields. They start small, but by summer they will tower over us. + prior knowledge will vary = The story is set on a farm in the springtime.

3. He still had a scar on his right hand from an unhappy hen pecking him last year. He had known Steve since the first grade. Daniel knew gathering eggs should not be the first chore a person performs. + prior knowledge will vary = Daniel is worried Steve will get hurt.

4. He had known Steve since the first grade. + prior knowledge will vary = Daniel and Steve are friends.

Morning Chores

Daniel looked over the chore board. Uncle Matt had suggested the boys work together on the chores, but when Daniel saw "collect eggs" on the list, he had a different idea. He still had a scar on his right hand from an unhappy hen pecking him last year. "No," Daniel thought, "gathering eggs is not for me."

When Steve joined him at the chore board, Daniel handed him an empty basket. "I'll bring you to Aunt Nancy's chicken coop," he said. "You can gather the eggs while I feed the pigs. Then, I'll come back to the coop, and we can deliver the eggs to my aunt. After that, we can finish the chores together. By the time we're finished, you'll know your way around here almost as well as I do."

Steve nodded, and the boys wandered off in the direction of the chicken coop. Along the way, Daniel pointed to rows of green plants and said, "Those are the cornfields."

"Those plants are short. I thought cornstalks were tall like the picture on our science book," Steve said.

Daniel laughed. "They start small, but by summer they will tower over us. After the corn is harvested, Uncle Matt cuts a maze into the field, and only a giant could find its way out by looking above the stalks. You'll have to come here with me again when I come back at Halloween."

When they arrived at the coop, Steve walked right inside. Daniel hesitated and before leaving shouted out, "Be careful! Don't get the hens riled up!"

Daniel raced up the hill to the pig pens and immediately went to work. When he finished his chore, he raced back down the hill to the chicken coop. He had known Steve since the first grade. Daniel knew gathering eggs should not be the first chore a person performs. He knew the ache in his gut wasn't from running.

Daniel felt better when he saw Steve. Steve stood outside the hen house holding a basketful of eggs and wearing a big grin. "I felt nervous when you shouted out a warning," Steve said. "The hens must be in a generous mood today because they didn't give me any trouble."

"Let's finish the chores," Daniel said. "I promised you some fun on this trip, and the sooner we finish the work, the sooner the fun begins."

Steve laughed. "Is this work?" he asked. "I'm already having fun!"

"Morning Chores" Graphic Organizer

Directions: Fill in the boxes to answer each question.

Why doesn't Daniel want to collect the eggs?

The story tells me:	+	I know:	=	So I think:

What is the setting of the story?

The story tells me:	+	I know:	=	So I think:

Why does Daniel have an "ache in his gut"?

The story tells me:	+	I know:	=	So I think:

Daniel and Steve are _____. (cousins, brothers, friends, neighbors)

The story tells me:	+	I know:	=	So I think:

 5

Directions: Picture Inferences

Individual ●

Reproduce Why Is the Boy Frowning? and Why Is the Boy Smiling? on pages 7 and 8 for each student. Remind students a reader sometimes uses clues in pictures to better understand what is happening. Direct the students' attention to the first illustration. Think aloud, "I see the boy is frowning. He is wearing a white baseball hat and shirt and carrying a bat. The other boys are wearing dark hats and shirts and look very happy. I know team members all wear the same uniform. I know teams are usually happier about winning than losing. I think the boy in the picture is frowning because he struck out and the other team is winning."

Ask students, "Have you ever frowned during or after a game or contest? Why? What were you feeling? Why do you think the boy in the picture is frowning?" Have students use what they see in the pictures and what they already know to answer the question on the lines provided. For additional practice, have students continue with Why Is the Boy Smiling?

Collect and review the papers, looking for responses that clearly answer the question and reflect the clues in the illustration. Review the inference process, and have students revise their answers, if necessary.

Small Group ● ●

Reproduce Draw Your Own Inference Picture on page 9 for each student. Ask students to think about a time they laughed. Where were they? Who were they with? What were they doing? Have students draw the scene in the blank box. Next, have students write a paragraph describing the scene on the lines below the picture. Remind students that the pictures should contain clues to why they are laughing.

Afterward, have students fold their papers in half so only the drawing is showing. Have each student trade pictures with a partner. On a separate sheet of paper, partners should write a paragraph describing the scene and explaining why the person in the drawing is laughing. Then, have students share and compare the paragraphs and discuss why they are alike or different. Ask students what clues in their partner's pictures helped them answer the question.

Whole Class ● ● ●

Reproduce two copies each of Why Is the Boy Frowning? and Why Is the Boy Smiling? on heavy paper. Cut the illustrations apart, and spread the cards faceup in two piles on a table in front of the class. You may also wish to include copies of photos from newspapers and magazines that show people expressing emotions. On the board, draw five columns. Label the columns: happy, sad, angry, afraid, and proud. Repeat the process on the other side of the board. Divide the class into two teams. Tell students to think about why the boy in the picture is crying or smiling. Have one member from each team come forward, select a picture, and tape it in the correct column. When the team member returns to the end of the line, the next player takes a turn. Explain that players need to find clues in the pictures and think about what they already know to decide what the boy in the picture is feeling. After teams finish, have them explain their choices to the class. The team with the most correct choices is the winner.

Why Is the Boy Frowning?

Directions: Study each picture. Then, answer the question, "Why is the boy frowning?" on the lines next to each picture.

_____

_____

_____

_____

_____

_____

_____

_____

_____

_____

_____

_____

  7

Why Is the Boy Smiling?

Name:_____

Directions: Study each picture. Then, answer the question, "Why is the boy smiling?" on the lines next to each picture.

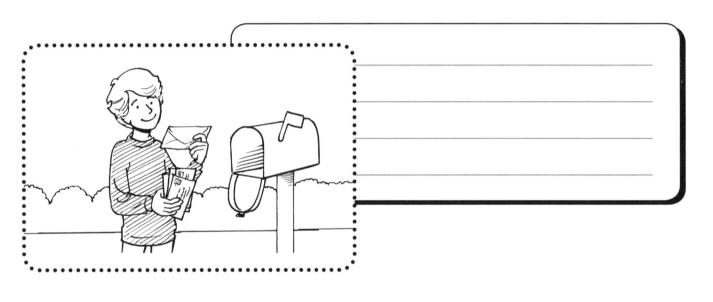

Draw Your Own Inference Picture

Name:_____

Directions: Think about a time you laughed. Where were you? What were you doing? Draw a picture of what happened. Then, write four or five sentences telling why you laughed.

Why is _____ **laughing?**

Directions: Inference Charades

Individual ●

Reproduce one set of Occupation Cards and one set of Wildlife Cards on pages 11 and 12. Cut the cards apart, and put them in a paper bag. Have each student pull one card from the bag. Then, have students write a paragraph describing the animal or occupation they chose without ever using the word or words on the card. Review paragraphs for descriptive details.

Small Group ● ●

Divide the class into groups of three or four students. Have students take turns reading the paragraphs they wrote in the Individual activity. After each paragraph is read, the other members of the group should guess what animal or occupation the paragraph describes.

After each paragraph is read, have students explain their guesses. What clues did they find in the paragraph? What did they already know that helped them determine the answer?

Whole Class ● ● ●

Reproduce one set of Occupation Cards. Cut the cards apart and place them in a paper bag. Choose one student to pull a card from the bag and act out the occupation. The rest of the class should try to guess the occupation. The student who correctly names the occupation first should explain to the class how he or she determined the answer. Then, that student should draw a new card and act out the occupation on the card.

Instead of acting out the occupation, the student can give verbal clues to the class, describing the occupation. In this format, explain that students must not use the words on the card when giving clues. Reproduce the Wildlife Cards for additional practice. Have students describe in detail the process they used to determine their answers.

Occupation Cards

astronaut

carpenter

cook

crossing guard

doctor

editor

fisherman

janitor

magician

farmer

musician

pilot

police officer

president

sailor

scientist

dentist

store clerk

artist

teacher

Wildlife Cards

chimpanzee	coyote	crab	cricket
crocodile	goose	parrot	polar bear
reindeer	seagull	seal	shark
skunk	swan	tiger	toad
turkey	walrus	woodpecker	worm

Directions: Who? What? Where?

Individual/Small Group

Read one or two of the riddles from Who? What? Where? Riddles on page 14 to the class. Point out the kinds of clues found in the riddles: "The clues about the eye describe what an eye does—sees and blinks—and how the word is spelled. The question, 'What am I?' tells us it is a thing."

Draw four lines on the board. Think aloud, "I am going to write a riddle about a tropical rain forest. What is special about a rain forest? The trees make oxygen for us to breathe." On the first line write, "This place is a breath of fresh air!" Think aloud, "What does it look like? I know rain forests have layers. One layer is the canopy, so I'll write 'Its canopy helps cool its floor' on the next line." Record the clue. Think aloud, "What is unusual about a rain forest? It is almost always raining." Write on the third line, "Don't forget your umbrella when you visit here!" On the last line, write "Where am I?" as you think aloud, "I know this is a place, so I will start my question with the word, 'Where.'" Repeat the process with another person, place, or thing. Have students suggest the clues.

Reproduce the Make Your Own Riddle worksheet on page 15 for each student. Have students work independently to write three new riddles. Have students write the answers to their riddles on the back of the worksheet. Collect and review the papers. Check to make sure the clues are focused and the answer can be inferred. Pass the papers back, and have students trade with a partner. Have partners write their guesses on the space provided. Then, have them check each other's work.

Small Group

Reproduce Who? What? Where? Riddles on page 14 for each student. Read the first riddle to the class. Ask what clues help them figure out the answer. Ask if anything they already knew helped them figure out the answer. Divide the class into pairs. Have student pairs work together to answer the riddles.

Collect and review the papers. Review the inference process with students who are having difficulty solving the riddles.

Whole Class ●●●

Divide the class into two teams. Use the students' original riddles from the Individual exercise, or provide a set of riddles for a game of Who? What? Where? Have one student read a riddle to the class. The first person to answer correctly earns a point for his or her team. Continue until each student has had an opportunity to read a riddle aloud. Have students explain how they determined their answers.

Answer Key

Who? What? Where? Riddles (Page 14)

1. eye
2. Abraham Lincoln
3. cornfield
4. pencil
5. Mother Goose
6. United States
7. merry-go-round/carousel
8. Martin Luther King Jr.
9. school
10. your age

Who? What? Where? Riddles

Name:_____

Directions: Read each riddle. Write the answer on the line below the riddle.

1 You can see through me.
I am spelled the same
  forward and backward.
I will hide if you blink.
What am I?

_____

2 I grew up in a log cabin.
I liked wearing a tall hat.
I am known for my honesty.
Who am I?

_____

3 No matter where I turn
  everything looks the same.
I must speak softly, because
  there are ears all around me.
I see a man hanging about with
  straw up his sleeves.
Where am I?

_____

4 I make it easy for you to
  change your mind.
I am very light for something
  filled with lead.
Most people think a
  number 2 is best.
What am I?

_____

5 I wrote about an egg called
  Humpty Dumpty.
I loved to write in rhyme as
  you can see.
Most children know a fine
  feathered me.
Who am I?

_____

6 All of its parts are not connected.
It stretches from the Atlantic
  to the Pacific.
Its capital has no state in
  this matter!
Where am I?

_____

7 I travel many miles every day,
  but I go nowhere.
I take people up and down
  and round and round.
My horses only like to trot
  when the music plays.
What am I?

_____

8 I had a dream for
  America.
I did not live long enough to
  see it come true.
People honor my memory
  in January.
Who am I?

_____

9 This is a place with real class.
It's really one for the books.
There are many rulers here!
Where am I?

_____

10 I go up, but I never come down!
Some people like to keep me
  a secret.
Others throw a party each time
  I change.
What am I?

_____

Make Your Own Riddle

Name:_____

Directions: Think about a person, place, or thing. Then, write the clues on the lines. Leave the answer blank.

 CLUES _____

_____

 _____

_____

What am I? _____

 _____

CLUES _____

 _____

_____

 _____

What am I? _____

 _____

CLUES _____

_____

_____

_____

What am I? _____

Directions: Using Clue Words

Individual

Write the words "cake," "candles," and "gifts" on the board. Draw a picture of a cake with candles on it, a sign with "Happy Birthday" written on it, a group of children wearing paper hats, one child blowing out the candles, and several gifts on the table. Think aloud, "When I look at my picture, I see some things like the cake and the candles are clue words. But some other things, like the birthday banner and the children, are things I inferred. I put together the clue words and what I already know about birthday parties and came up with a new idea." Ask the students to find something else in the picture that shows you put the clues together with what you already knew.

Reproduce Read, Think, Draw! 1 on page 17 for each student. Read the directions with the class. Then, have students complete the drawings and questions independently.

Collect and review the papers. Look for evidence that the student understands the difference between what is directly stated and what is inferred. Also, evaluate the student's ability to make a reasonable inference.

Small Group

Divide the class into groups of three or four students. Reproduce Read, Think, Draw! 2 on page 18 for each student. Distribute the

pages, and have the students use the first set of clues to draw a picture and answer the questions. When they finish, have students share their pictures and discuss the questions with the members of the group.

Next, have each student read the second set of clues and draw the picture. Then, have each student trade papers with someone in his or her group and answer the questions based on that drawing. When completed, students should share the picture with the group and explain their answers.

Collect and review the papers. Check to make sure the answers reflect an understanding of the difference between directly stated and inferred information. Listen to the students' explanations of their answers.

Whole Class

Divide the class into three or four groups. Provide each group with a Read, Think, Draw! page, a piece of poster board, pencils, and crayons or markers. Have students work together within their group to read the clues and draw the setting. When finished, display the drawings. Read the questions to the class, and discuss each drawing as a class.

Listen for evidence that the students understand the difference between directly stated information and inferred information. Ask students to explain how they made an inference.

Read, Think, Draw! 1

Name:_____

Directions: Read the clue words. Use the words to draw a picture of the setting. Then, look at your picture and answer the questions.

CLUE WORDS:

snow

skate

people

Which things in your picture are clue words?

_____

Which things show you used the clues and what you already knew?

_____

CLUE WORDS:

computers

bookshelves

woman

Which things in your picture are clue words?

_____

Which things show you used the clues and what you already knew?

_____

Read, Think, Draw! 2

Name:_____

Directions: Read the clue words. Use the words to draw a picture of the setting. Then, look at your picture and answer the questions.

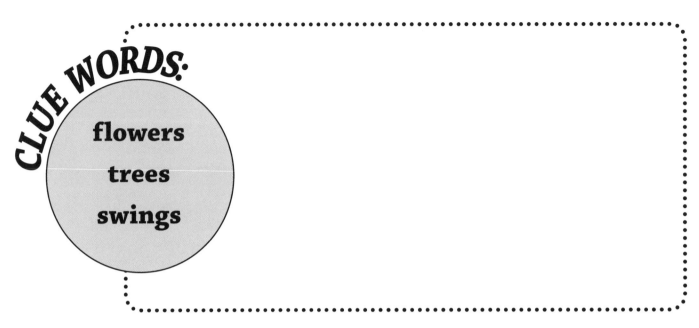

CLUE WORDS:

flowers

trees

swings

Which things in your picture are clue words?

_____

Which things show you used the clues and what you already knew?

_____

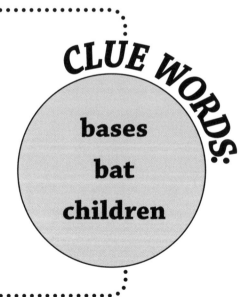

CLUE WORDS:

bases

bat

children

Which things in your picture are clue words?

_____

Which things show you used the clues and what you already knew?

_____

Directions: I See, Therefore, I Think

Individual

Reproduce I See, I Think 1 and 2 on pages 20 and 21 for each student. Distribute the pages, and then draw the students' attention to the first illustration. On the board, write the following sentences, "There is a boy, a girl, a man, and a woman. There is a family." Think aloud, "When I look at the picture, I see a boy, a girl, a man, and a woman. I think they are a family because there are adults and children together, and they remind me of families I know." Next, write the following sentences on the board "The children are eating cotton candy. There is a roller coaster and other rides in the picture. The woman is holding tickets and pointing at the roller coaster. The family is going to ride the roller coaster at the carnival." Ask the students which sentences are things they see in the picture. Ask students which sentences show new ideas inferred from the pictures. Then, have students complete the other examples independently.

When all students have finished, collect and review the papers. Sentences should clearly show an understanding of the difference between what is directly pictured and what has been inferred.

Small Group

Have each student draw a picture of an event from real life or a story he or she has read. Next, have each student trade pictures with a partner. Each partner should write four sentences about the picture. Two sentences should be about things the student sees in his or her partner's picture. Two sentences should be about things the student infers from his or her partner's picture. When finished, one student should read the sentences aloud to the partner. The partner states whether the sentence is an "I See" or an "I Think" sentence. The students then discuss the answers and reverse roles.

Collect and review the papers. Check to make sure the answers reflect an understanding of the difference between what is pictured and what is inferred.

Whole Class

Prior to class, reproduce the illustrations on transparencies. On index cards, write two or three observations and two or three inferences about each illustration, one per card. Put all of the cards for each illustration into four separate paper bags.

Divide the class into two teams. Display the first illustration on the overhead, and pull a card from the coordinating bag. Read the sentence aloud, and state whether the sentence says something you see in the picture or an idea you get from the picture. Explain your answer. Have a student from the first team pull another card from the bag, read the sentence, state whether the sentence tells something he or she sees in the picture or an idea that comes from the picture, and explain his or her answer. Repeat the process with a member of the other team and a new card. Rotate between teams, and award a point for each correct answer. Adjust the number of sentence cards so each member of the class has an opportunity to participate.

Listen for evidence that the students understand the difference between observation and inference.

I See, I Think 1

Name:_____

Directions: Look at the pictures. Under each picture, write two sentences telling what you see in the picture. Then, write two sentences telling things you infer from the picture.

I see ⋯⋯▶ _____

_____

I think ⋯⋯▶ _____

_____

I see ⋯⋯▶ _____

_____

I think ⋯⋯▶ _____

_____

I See, I Think 2

Name:_____

Directions: Look at the pictures. Under each picture, write two sentences telling what you see in the picture. Then, write two sentences telling things you infer from the picture.

I see ····▶ _____

_____

I think ····▶ _____

_____

I see ····▶ _____

_____

I think ····▶ _____

_____

Directions: Inferring Feelings

Individual ●

Reproduce and distribute How Do I Feel? 1 and 2 on pages 23 and 24. Have students read the passages independently and use the word bank to answer the questions that follow on the lines provided. Remind students to look for clues in the story and add them to what they already know to come up with the correct answer. Collect and review the papers.

Small Group ● ●

Divide the class into groups of three or four students. Reproduce and distribute one of the How Do I Feel? pages. Have the students read the passages and discuss the answers within their group. Next, have each student write a paragraph. Remind students the paragraph should show but not tell how the character in the story feels. At the bottom of the paper, the student should write how the character feels. Have each student read the paragraph, but not the answer, to the group. The other members of the group listen to the story and determine how the character feels. Have them discuss the clues in the passage that made them think that.

Collect and review the papers. Check to make sure the answers can be inferred from the information in the paragraph. Listen to the group discussions.

Whole Class ● ● ●

Write the following words on the board: happy, sad, angry, afraid, surprised, and sleepy. Read aloud the passages on the How Do I Feel? pages. After each passage, ask students how the main character feels. Have students explain their answers. Tape the passage under the feeling word it describes.

Next, divide the class into two teams and have students write a paragraph that shows, but does not tell, how their characters feel (happy, sad, angry, afraid, surprised, or sleepy). Have each team write on different colored paper. Post a set of the target feeling words in two separate areas of the classroom. Collect the paragraphs, and trade them with the opposing teams. Have team members take turns reading the paragraphs. As a team, members should decide which feeling is expressed in the paragraph and post the paragraph under the correct label. Play stops when a team has posted all of their paragraphs. Review the answers and discuss as a class. The first team to correctly sort the paragraphs and explain their answers wins.

Listen to the students' answers and explanations for evidence of their understanding of the inference process and their ability to apply the process to the written word.

Answer Key

How Do I Feel? 1 (Page 23)	How Do I Feel? 2 (Page 24)
1. sleepy	1. angry
2. sad	2. happy
3. surprised	3. afraid

How Do I Feel? 1

Name:_____

Directions: Read each story. Use a feeling from the word bank to answer each question.

Margaret looked across the aisle at Lucy. Her friend was slumped against the bus wall with her cheek pressed against the glass. She was snoring so loudly everyone could hear her over the hum of the bus. Margaret didn't know if she snored too, but she knew this was not the way she wanted to find out. She sat up straight and rubbed her eyes. It had been a long day, but they were almost home. She just needed to keep her eyelids from closing for a little while longer.

How does Margaret feel? _____

Drew sat on the floor of his empty bedroom. Everything else was in the moving van now. They had packed his furniture, his books, his trophies, and his clothes. He looked around the room and remembered the sleepovers, the card games, and the planning he had enjoyed there with Marc. Drew knew they would keep in touch, but that wouldn't be the same as seeing Marc every day. Drew rested his forehead against his knees. He thought about how much he would miss his best friend.

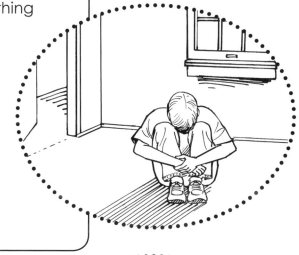

How does Drew feel? _____

Elena went outside to get the mail. She carried the pile inside and set it on the counter. She was about to walk away when something caught her attention. Her eyes widened. On top of the pile, there was a letter addressed to her! She hardly ever got mail. Elena could hardly believe it.

How does Elena feel? _____

happy	angry	surprised
sad	afraid	sleepy

Name:_____

Directions: Read each story. Use a feeling from the word bank to answer each question.

Sal threw the rubber ball at the brick wall. It bounced off the bricks and shot back at him. "Are you trying to knock that giant wall down with that tiny ball?" Jamal asked.

Sal glared in Jamal's direction and grunted.

"What's wrong?" Jamal asked.

"Last month, my brother said if I would do both of our chores, then this month he would do them all. I did our chores, but now he doesn't want to hold up his end of the bargain. It isn't fair!"

How does Sal feel? _____

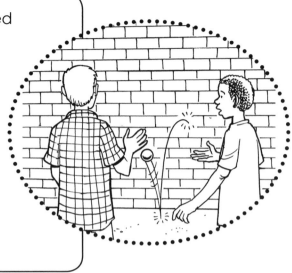

Jillian stretched out her arms and tipped her face toward the sky. After a solid week of rain, the warmth of the sun's rays felt great against her skin. Jillian heard the birds singing and the breeze whispering through the trees. She started down the park's path. When she reached the field, she saw there were enough people to play her favorite game—kickball. A smile spread across her face as she thought, "This is my lucky day!"

How does Jillian feel? _____

Thomas gripped the horn on the saddle so tight his knuckles turned white. He had never ridden a horse before and had not anticipated sitting so high above the ground. The horse snorted and took a few steps backward toward the lake. "Help!" Thomas shouted. "How do I get this horse out of reverse and moving in the right direction?"

How does Thomas feel? _____

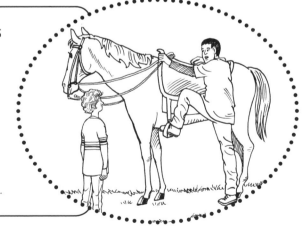

happy	angry	surprised
sad	afraid	sleepy

Directions: Inferring Action

Individual ●

Reproduce What Am I Doing? 1 and 2 on pages 26 and 27 for each student. Have students read each passage independently and answer the question that follows. Remind students to use clues in the story and prior knowledge to come up with the correct answer. Then, have them draw a picture in each box of the action described. Discuss the activity as a class when all students are finished. What words helped them determine the answers?

Small Group ● ●

Divide the class into groups of four or five students. Reproduce What Am I Doing? 1 or 2 for each group. Cut the passages out, and place them facedown in the center of each group. Have students work in pairs to read and act out the passages. Explain that while one partner is reading the words, the other partner will become a "living picture" by completing the actions described. The other group members will then try to guess the activity. After the group finishes all of the passages, they should discuss how both the words and the actions helped them determine the correct answer.

Whole Class ● ● ●

Draw a flowchart on the board. Place three open squares in a column and one open square to the right of the column. Draw an arrow from the column to the square on the right. Read aloud the first passage and question on What Am I Doing? 1. Ask a student to tell one clue in the description that will help the class answer the question, "What am I doing?" Record the answer in the first box in the left column. Continue until the entire left column is filled. Then, ask a student what answer would be supported by those clues. Record the answer in the box on the right. Repeat the process with the second passage.

Next, divide the class into teams of four students. Have each team draw a flowchart on the board and line up in front of their chart. Explain that after you read a passage aloud, the first three students in line will go to the board one at a time and fill in a clue box, and the last student will use the clues to help them answer the question, "What am I doing?" The first team to correctly complete the chart wins a point. Continue play with the passages on What Am I Doing? 2 or passages from grade-level books. Have students rotate line positions, so each student has an opportunity to answer the question.

Look at the flowcharts for evidence of students' understanding of the inference process and their ability to apply the process to the written word.

Answer Key

What Am I Doing? 1 (Page 26)
1. sharpening a pencil
2. making a sandwich
3. playing baseball

What Am I Doing? 2 (Page 27)
1. raking leaves
2. swimming
3. building a treehouse

What Am I Doing? 1

Directions: Read each paragraph. Draw lines under the words in the story that help you answer the question. Then, write your answer on the line and draw a picture of the action in the box provided.

I slide one end of the yellow stick into the small hole and hold it in place with my left hand. I grasp a small handle with my right hand and move my right hand up and down in the shape of a circle. I hear the sound of metal scraping against wood. I pause, pull out the stick, and check my progress by examining the point. Then, I place it back in the hole and crank the handle again.

What am I doing? _____

I place two slices of bread on a plate and spread mustard on one side of each slice. Next, I take a slice of ham, fold it, and place it on top of the mustard on one slice of bread. Then, I add a few more slices and a slice of cheese. Next, I place some lettuce leaves on top of the cheese. Finally, I place the second slice of bread on top of the lettuce with the mustard facing down.

What am I doing? _____

I step up to the plate and nod to the umpire. I adjust my helmet before bending my knees and lifting my arms. I focus my attention on the mound and prepare for the first pitch. It's fast and outside, so I let it go by. I watch as the boy on the mound winds up and throws the ball right down the center. I swing and start to run as I hear the sound of the leather smack against the wood.

What am I doing? _____

What Am I Doing? 2

Directions: Read each paragraph. Draw lines under the words in the story that help you answer the question. Then, write your answer on the line and draw a picture of the action in the box provided.

I start under the trees where most of the work is located in the fall. I grip the long, thin handle and place the other end of my tool on the ground. I scrape it across the ground toward my body. Then, I lift it and place it further away from me again. I repeat this process many times until there is a big pile in front of me. I move the crunchy, colorful pile into a tall bag and drag it to the curb.

What am I doing? _____

I jump right in and get wet from my head to my toes. Then, I push off with my feet from the wall and start reaching forward with my cupped right hand. As my right hand pulls back, my left arm stretches out in front of me and cuts smoothly into the water. At the same time, I kick from my hips; first my right leg goes up and my left leg goes down. Then, I reverse the position of my legs and kick up and down to propel myself forward.

What am I doing? _____

I search the backyard for a big, strong tree. Next, I make my plans for what it is going to look like. Then, I make a list of supplies I will need. Then, I gather my tools and bring home my supplies from the store. I start by building a platform. Next, I build walls and leave room for windows. Then, I put a roof on. Lastly, I build steps leading up to a door in the floor.

What am I doing? _____

Individual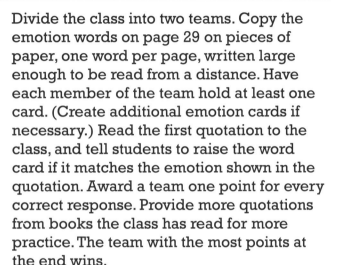

Reproduce How Am I Feeling? Quotes on page 29 for each student. Have students read the quotations independently and draw a line between the quotation and the word that matches the feeling the quotation shows. Remind students to read the quote and think about when and why they might say something like it. When all students have finished, discuss the answers as a class.

Small Group

Reproduce How Am I Feeling? Quotes for each pair of students. Divide the class into groups of four students and each group into two pairs. Cut the copies in half lengthwise, so one person holds the quotations, and the other person holds the emotion words. Give one member of each pair a list of quotations, and give the partner the list of words. Explain that inference can also be used when listening or reading text out loud. Play begins with a student reading the first quotation to his partner. If the partner identifies the correct emotion word, the pair receives a point and play rotates to the other pair. All players must agree the emotion stated is correct and be ready to defend their answers with examples. If the team member gives an incorrect answer, play goes to the other team, but the same quotation is used. The pair with the most points wins.

Whole Class

Divide the class into two teams. Copy the emotion words on page 29 on pieces of paper, one word per page, written large enough to be read from a distance. Have each member of the team hold at least one card. (Create additional emotion cards if necessary.) Read the first quotation to the class, and tell students to raise the word card if it matches the emotion shown in the quotation. Award a team one point for every correct response. Provide more quotations from books the class has read for more practice. The team with the most points at the end wins.

Discuss both correct and incorrect responses. Ask students to explain their answers.

Answer Key

How Am I Feeling? Quotes (Page 29)

1. lonely
2. angry
3. afraid
4. surprised
5. sleepy

6. shy
7. confused
8. excited
9. proud
10. sad

How Am I Feeling? Quotes

Name:_____

Directions: Draw a line between the sentence and the feeling it shows. Use each word once.

① "I really miss my brother when he is away at college."

② "You were wrong to take my things without my permission!"

③ "I can't look down; this bridge is too high for me."

④ "This isn't what I was expecting!"

⑤ "I can barely pry open my eyes. Do I have to get out of bed so early?"

⑥ "I think you should give the speech. I'm uncomfortable talking in front of strangers."

⑦ "I thought we needed to go this direction, but the sign points that way. What should we do?"

⑧ "I can't wait until the concert begins!"

⑨ "It took me months to build this, but look how beautifully it turned out."

⑩ "I'm trying not to cry, but this storm has ruined our entire vacation."

afraid

angry

confused

excited

lonely

proud

sad

shy

sleepy

surprised

Directions: Describing Places

Individual

Reproduce Be the Writer 1 and 2 on pages 31 and 32 for each student. Read the directions with the class. Then, have students independently read each description of a place and write two more sentences describing the place. Remind students to use the sentences as well as what they already know about each place to help them write their own sentences. Have volunteers read their sentences to the class.

Small Group ●●

Divide the class into pairs. Reproduce Be the Writer 1 for each pair of students. Read the directions with the class. Then, have one member of each pair read the description of a place. Each student adds a sentence to the description and explains what clues in the text or prior knowledge helped him or her decide what to write. Students take turns reading and writing until each description is completed. Hold a class discussion when the activity is complete. Listen to the students' justifications of their answers.

Whole Class ●●●

Reproduce Be the Writer 1 and 2 on transparencies. Display the first description. Tell students they will use the information in the sentences plus what they already know to write more sentences describing the place. Read the first description aloud. Ask students to silently write two additional sentences for the paragraph. After everyone has had an opportunity to share his or her sentence, discuss how the sentences differed. Ask students to explain how they came up with their ideas. Repeat the process with several more descriptions.

Be the Writer 1

Directions: A school wants to print a guide for visitors and needs your help. Read each set of sentences. Then, write two more sentences describing the place. Use what the sentences tell you and what you already know to write the new sentences.

1 **Our school contains many smaller sections and spaces. A long hallway divides each wing into two equal parts. On either side of the hall are entrances to classrooms. Ceiling lights help keep the hallways bright and cheerful.**

_____

_____

2 **The library is one of the largest rooms in the school. Bookcases brimming with books line the walls. The signs on the cases help students and teachers find the books they need. The librarian has a special workspace in the library.**

_____

_____

3 **One of the busiest places in our school is the cafeteria. This place is broken into two main parts. In one area, cooks prepare and serve the food. In the other area, students and teachers enjoy healthy lunches.**

_____

_____

4 **Another popular place in school is the gym. Some things, like the mats on the walls, never seem to change. However, other things, such as the sports equipment on the gym floor, are always changing.**

_____

_____

Be the Writer 2

Directions: A school wants to print a guide for visitors and needs your help. Read each set of sentences. Then, write two more sentences describing the place. Use what the sentences tell you and what you already know to write the new sentences.

1 **Visitors to our school always report to the main office first. The people who work there help keep the school running smoothly. A quick look around the office gives many hints to what takes place there.**

_____

_____

2 **Our school has a health center. In some ways, it looks like any other office. There is a desk and a set of filing cabinets. However, the health center has many things you would not find in the main office, such as beds.**

_____

_____

3 **Many students love spending time in the computer lab. There are many computers in the room. The teacher helps keep the rows of monitor screens and keyboards clean. There is a chair in front of each work station.**

_____

_____

4 **No trip to our school is complete without a stop at the playground. At lunchtime this is a very busy place. Often, a group of children is jumping rope or playing tag. Sometimes children practice basketball shots using the hoops on the playground.**

_____

_____

Directions: Figuring Out What Happens Next

Individual ⚪

Reproduce What Next? on page 34 for each student. Read the directions with the class. Then, have students work independently to complete the activity. Remind students to use what they see in the picture plus what they already know to decide or infer what the character in the picture will do next. Discuss the answers as a class.

Small Group ⚪⚪

Reproduce What Next? and give one to each pair. Have each student complete the activity independently. Then, explain that students will study the pictures and make a second inference about each picture. They will use the inference to ask their partners a question. Think aloud, "In the first picture, I see the sun is shining through the window. I see the girl is dressed in day clothes. I know the sun shines in the daytime in most places. I know it is usually dark at night, so I can infer this is taking place in the morning. I can ask my partner when the activity takes place."

Tell the students to write their questions on a separate sheet of paper. Partners trade papers and answer each other's questions. When finished, they can compare answers. Collect and review the papers. Look for signs in both the questions and answers that point to the inference process.

Whole Class ⚫⚫⚫

Reproduce What Next? on a transparency. Display the first illustration. Ask students what they know about the girl in the illustration. Lead the discussion with question prompts, such as, "Where is she? What time of day do you think it is? What is she going to do?" Record the students' answers and ask them to explain their reasoning.

Divide the class into two or three groups. Display the second illustration. Have students work with their group to list ideas about the character in the illustration. Later, have groups share and compare their lists. Ask why the lists might not be the same.

Answer Key

What Next? (Page 34)

1. b, answers will vary
2. a, answers will vary
3. d, answers will vary
4. c, answers will vary

What Next?

Directions: Look at each picture. Circle the letter before the correct answer.
Then, write how you know the answer.

1

What will the girl do next?

a) go to sleep

b) make the bed

c) water the plants

d) walk the dog

How do you know?

2

What will the girl do next?

a) blow out the candles

b) feed the goldfish

c) blow up balloons

d) take a photograph

How do you know?

3

What will the boy do next?

a) ride his bike

b) throw the ball

c) go in the dog house

d) paint the dog house

How do you know?

4

What will the boy do next?

a) play football

b) shovel snow

c) eat breakfast

d) write a letter

How do you know?

Directions: Reading for Relationships

Individual ●

Reproduce Independent Reading 1 and 2 on pages 36 and 37 for each student. Read the directions with the class. Then, have students work independently to read each passage and answer the question. Have them underline the clues in the text that help them figure out the relationship. Remind students to use clues from the text plus what they already know to infer the relationship between the characters. Collect and review the papers.

Whole Class ● ● ●

Divide the class into groups of six. Explain that each group will work together to write three to five clues pointing to a relationship. Model the process. Think aloud, "If I wanted to let someone know two people were neighbors I might start with, 'In the summer at night, Pam and I would sit by our bedroom windows and whisper across the alley to each other.' Then I would add, 'In the daytime, we sat on our porches talking into paper cups tied together by a long string.' For my third clue, 'We always drew a hopscotch board half in front of my house and half in front of hers so it would belong to both of us.'" Then, ask students if they think you and Pam were sisters, cousins, neighbors, or classmates.

On the board, write the following list: two cousins; two sisters; a parent and child; a grandparent and grandchild; a teacher and student; two friends. Tell groups of students to work together to make a list of three to five clues for each of the relationships. When they have finished, have groups share their lists with the class, while the other groups try to determine the relationship.

Small Group ● ●

Divide the class into pairs of students. Have each student write a paragraph describing his or her relationship with a family member, friend, classmate, or teacher, without saying who the person is in the text. Then, have students exchange paragraphs and guess who they are written about. Tell students to underline any clues that tell them who the people are.

Answer Key

Independent Reading 1 (Page 36)	Independent Reading 2 (Page 37)
1. c	1. d
2. b	2. a

Independent Reading 1

Directions: Read each story. Then, answer the question.

The boys looked at the two plain layer cakes on the counter. "I'll decorate one cake for my mother's birthday, and you can decorate the other cake for your mother's birthday," George said.

"Okay," answered Nick. "Let's decorate them in the same way. Since our mothers are twins, they should have twin cakes!"

The boys gathered the ingredients on the counter. George said, "I'm not sure our plan is the best one. My mother likes a custard filling, and your mother likes a fruit filling."

"That's true," Nick nodded. "Let's use different fillings, but still decorate them alike."

When the cakes were finished, Nick and George admired their creations. Nick announced, "These are perfect for our mothers—identical on the outside, but a little different on the inside!"

1 **What best describes Nick and George?**

   a) twins

   b) friends

   c) cousins

   d) brothers

Tracy pushed her favorite chair into the corner of the porch where the sunlight collected. She settled into the chair and opened her book. After reading a few pages, she paused to soak in some of the sunshine. Tracy noticed Mrs. White, who was about the same age as Tracy's grandmother, planting flowers in her front yard. "Mrs. White looks like she is having a difficult time with her plants," Tracy thought.

Tracy put down her book and walked across the street. "Can I help you?" she asked Mrs. White. "I love to dig and plant, and I'm good at taking directions. Just tell me what you want planted in each location, and I'll do the work."

2 **What best describes Tracy and Mrs. White?**

   a) strangers

   b) neighbors

   c) student and teacher

   d) granddaughter and grandmother

Independent Reading 2

Directions: Read each story. Then, answer each question.

Phil grasped the bat and bent his knees slightly as he watched Manny wave the outfielders further back. "I played with your older brother back in high school," Manny said. "He could knock a ball right out of the park."

Phil inhaled deeply. He didn't want Manny's expectations of his ability to be too high. Phil was certain he was not in the same league of players that his brother had been. Phil watched as the pitcher released the ball. He swung hard but caught nothing but air as the ball whizzed over home plate.

"Shake it off. This is why we have these practices. Relax and let the ball come to you," Manny instructed from his perch behind the fence.

Phil nodded and waited for the next pitch. He knew his skills would improve this season if he listened to Manny's advice.

1 **What best describes Phil and Manny?**

   a) brothers

   b) strangers

   c) son and father

   d) player and coach

Molly knocked on Kate's door. She said, "Mom said to be ready for ballet class in 15 minutes."

Kate danced in a studio on the other side of town. The 40-minute round trip meant having to stay at the studio while Kate danced. Molly didn't mind though. She enjoyed helping out as long as it meant getting hold of the keys to the family car. Fifteen minutes later, the always-prompt Kate flew past her. "Hurry, Molly!" she shouted. "Tonight Ms. Fontaine is giving out parts for the spring ballet."

Molly grabbed her math book and the car keys and followed Kate out the door.

2 **What best describes Molly and Kate?**

   a) sisters

   b) classmates

   c) mother and daughter

   d) teacher and student

Individual ●

Reproduce "It's for the Birds" and "It's for the Birds" Questions on pages 39 and 40 for each student. Explain to the class that they will use the information in the graph and passage, plus what they already know, to infer the answer to each question. When all students have finished, ask them to share their answers. Discuss what information in the graph or text helped them know the correct answer. Repeat the process with "The Science Project" on pages 41 and 42.

Whole Class ● ● ●

Reproduce "It's for the Birds" and "The Science Project" on a transparency. Divide the class into two teams. Display the "It's for the Birds" graph and read the text. Then, read the first question associated with it and model the inference process. Think aloud, "I see by looking at the graph that six different kinds of birds eat sunflower seeds, three types eat safflower seeds, three types eat suet, and only two eat nectar. I know if I want to draw the biggest mix of birds, I need to use the feed that appeals to the most kinds of birds. So putting together the clues from the graph and what I already know, I can infer sunflower seeds would be my best choice."

Have one student from each team stand. Ask the second question aloud. The first standing student to answer correctly scores two points for his or her team. As the question is asked, have other team members record the question number and answer on a separate sheet of paper. After the standing student answers, ask how many students agree with the answer. Then, the student standing for the other team can earn his or her team one point by stating the information used to infer the answer and where the information was found (graph, text, or both). Continue the process, rotating standing students. Repeat with the second graph set.

Answer Key

"It's for the Birds" Questions (Page 40)	"The Science Project" Questions (Page 42)
1. a	1. a
2. c	2. a
3. d	3. b
4. b	4. d
5. d	5. b
6. c	6. c

It's for the Birds

The fourth-grade students at Pine Elementary School studied birds last month. They set up bird feeders in four different places around the school. They used a different bird feed in each feeder. The students spent $100 for three sacks of sunflower seeds, two sacks of safflower seeds, six bottles of nectar, and six cans of suet fat. They changed the seeds every week. The store clerk warned them moldy food can make the birds sick. The students decided to change the suet and nectar every three days. During recess, students watched the feeders. They noted the number of birds and kinds of birds visiting the feeders for a month. Read the bar graphs. Then answer the questions on the next page.

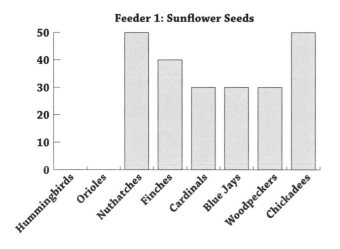

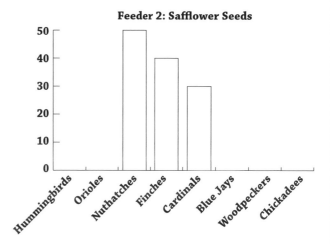

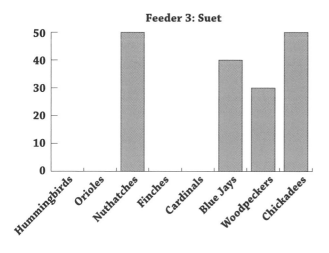

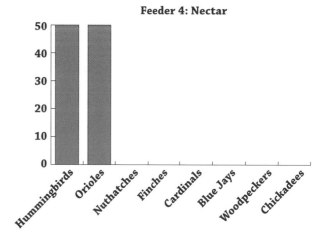

"It's for the Birds" Questions

Name:_____

Directions: Use the graphs and the story to answer the questions.

1 **What feed should you use to get the biggest mix of birds?**

   a) sunflower seeds

   b) safflower seeds

   c) nectar

   d) suet

2 **What feed should you use if you do not want woodpeckers near your home?**

   a) suet or nectar

   b) sunflower seeds or suet

   c) nectar or safflower seeds

   d) sunflower or safflower seeds

3 **At the end of the month, Ms. Green's class voted to use nectar for the rest of the year.**

What most likely were their favorite birds to watch?

   a) finches

   b) cardinals

   c) woodpeckers

   d) hummingbirds

4 **Why did they change the nectar and suet more often than the seeds?**

   a) They got eaten faster.

   b) They got moldy faster.

   c) They drew more birds.

   d) They had less seeds.

5 **Why don't the graphs show night-feeding birds?**

   a) The fourth grade only studied a few birds.

   b) The birds can't find the feeders at night.

   c) Students remove the feed each night.

   d) Students are not at school then.

6 **Why did the students see more nuthatches than any other kind of bird?**

   a) Nuthatches were the biggest birds they watched.

   b) The fourth graders raised nuthatches.

   c) Nuthatches eat more kinds of feed.

   d) The feeders were easier for the nuthatches to reach.

The Science Project

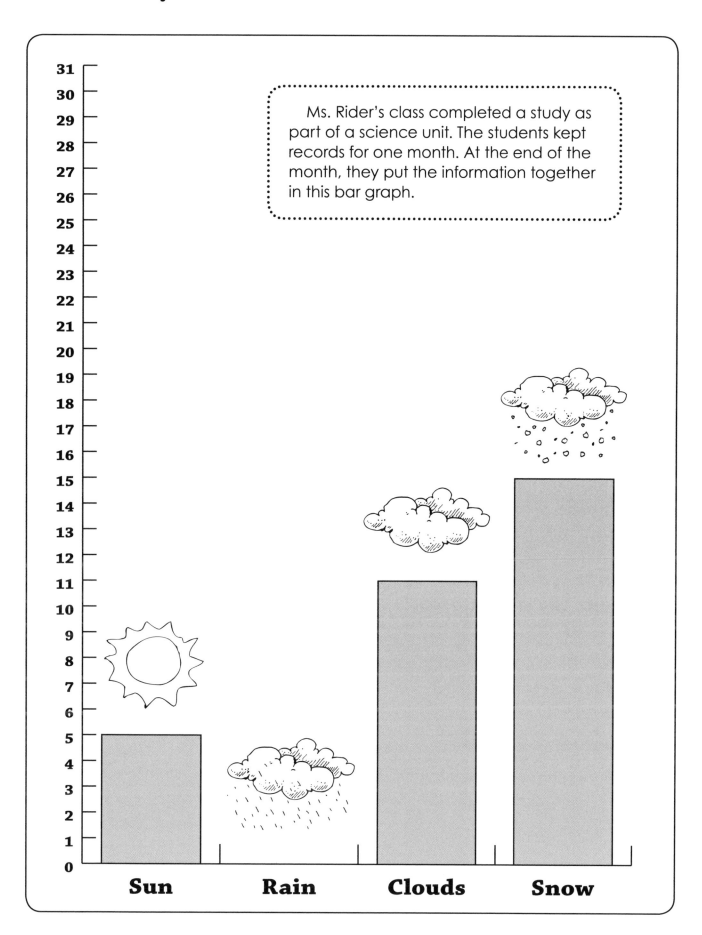

Ms. Rider's class completed a study as part of a science unit. The students kept records for one month. At the end of the month, they put the information together in this bar graph.

Sun   Rain   Clouds   Snow

"The Science Project" Questions

Directions: Use the graph and the story to answer the questions.

1 **During what month do you think the students worked on this project?**

  a) January

  b) August

  c) June

  d) July

2 **What would the students wear most often to school this month?**

  a) warm coats

  b) rain coats

  c) shorts

  d) sandals

3 **Where do the students most likely live?**

  a) Hawaii

  b) Maine

  c) Florida

  d) Arizona

4 **What did the students most likely do after school?**

  a) build sand castles

  b) plant flower seeds

  c) play softball

  d) build snowmen

5 **What topic was the class studying in science?**

  a) plants

  b) weather

  c) calendars

  d) measurement

6 **Why do you think there aren't any rainy days on the graph?**

  a) It only rained on weekends.

  b) It never rains in that area.

  c) It was too cold.

  d) It was too hot.

Directions: In the News

Individual

Reproduce the "One for the Records" and "Fourth-Grader Wins Award" articles and questions on pages 44–47. Have students read the articles and answer the questions independently. Ask students to highlight or underline the information in the articles that helped them answer the questions. Remind students they will need to put together information in the articles and what they already know to infer the correct answer. Collect and review the papers.

Small Group

After completing the Individual activity, break students into groups of three. Reproduce The Daily News on page 48 for each student. Have each student write a fake news story about a world record (or research a real one). When finished, tell each student to pass his or her paper to the student who is sitting on his or her right. Next, have the students read the articles they received and write three or four inference questions. Remind students the clues to the answers must be in the story, but not the answers themselves. After they finish, have students pass their papers to the right again. This time, the students should read the stories, answer the questions, and highlight or underline the clues in the story. Finally, the papers are passed again to the right to the original writer, who reviews the questions and answers. Students then discuss the inferences made and the clues and prior knowledge used to make the inferences. Collect and review the papers. Listen to the students' discussions of the answers.

Answer Key

"One for the Records" Questions (Page 45)	"Fourth-Grader Wins Award" Questions (Page 47)
1. a	1. c
2. d	2. a
3. b	3. b
4. c	4. d
5. a	5. a
6. b	6. a

One for the Records

Did you know there are world records for just about anything you can think of? Some people set goals to set or break records, no matter how unusual or difficult the goals might be. Some people break records without even trying. Either way, learning about different world records can be interesting.

In the farming town of Pulpi, Spain, a group of people wanted to set a world record. They decided to meet this goal by doing what they did best—growing vegetables. Twenty people got together at the town's fairgrounds. They mixed lettuce and tomatoes. They added onions, peppers, and olives. The result was a world-record salad. It weighed almost 15,000 pounds! Restaurants served the salad for free to diners.

A man in Northern Ireland set his sights on breaking a record when he heard a city in England held an interesting record. It was for the most Santa Clauses gathered in one place. The jolly total was 3,921 people. They were all dressed as Santa or as Santa's helper. The people of Derry City decided they could beat that. They held an event in September 2007. They brought 12,965 Santas to town! This made Northern Ireland the merry record holder. It also raised money for the needy.

Not all records are made by a group of people. Some are held by individuals. For example, a man in the United States is the fastest clapper. He can clap his hands 721 times in a single minute. That's 12 claps per second! Another man holds the record for the longest distance walked while balancing a milk bottle on his head. He walked almost 81 miles! It took him 23 hours and 35 minutes. This man really loves the "est" suffix. He holds 14 different world records! If you want to break his milk bottle record, practice first with a plastic bottle. It is much safer!

Some records are set without even trying. A family in Missouri raises miniature horses. These horses grow to be about 34 inches tall. About five years ago, a tiny colt was born. It started small and only grew for one year. Now, fully grown, the horse is only 17 inches tall. She is the smallest horse on record. The horse wears special braces on her legs, because her legs are too small to hold up the weight of her head and body. Her owners have to watch what she eats too, so she doesn't eat too much.

If you want to find out more about unusual world records, read books or search the Internet. You'll be amazed at what you'll find!

"One for the Records" Questions

Directions: Circle the letter of the correct answer for each question.

1 Why did the people of Pulpi choose to make a world-record salad?

a) Local farms grew those foods.

b) The restaurants needed the salad.

c) They had never eaten salad before.

d) It was the only record that had never been broken.

2 Why did they make the salad at the fairgrounds?

a) They grew the plants there.

b) They wanted to keep it a secret.

c) They wanted to sell the salad there.

d) They needed a big space to work.

3 Why did the people dress as Santa to go to Derry?

a) They wanted to celebrate Christmas.

b) They wanted to help break a record.

c) They always dressed as Santa.

d) They couldn't get to England.

4 Why should you practice walking with a plastic bottle on your head?

a) Plastic bottles hold more milk.

b) Milk in glass bottles costs more.

c) A glass bottle will break when it falls.

d) Plastic bottles are easier to balance.

5 Why don't the smallest horse's owners want it to eat too much?

a) Gaining more weight will be too much for its legs.

b) They don't want another horse to beat the record.

c) They want the food for their other horses.

d) The horse's legs might grow much longer.

6 Why is the horse's record different from the other records in the story?

a) The horse's record is based on size.

b) The horse or its owners didn't set out to make or break a world record.

c) The record for the smallest horse is the easiest world record to break.

d) The horse set the record in the United States.

THE DAILY NEWS

News You Can Use!

Fourth-Grader Wins Award

Mayor Thomas presented the Wilder Award for Writing on Monday. The contest is open to all students in grades 4–12 in Maryland. The judges needed weeks to read the entries. This year's winner was a real surprise. It is Laura Cole, a fourth-grade student at Mountain Ridge School. She entered an essay about her trip to Washington, D.C. Laura is the youngest writer to earn the top award.

Laura explained how she did it. "The rules for the contest stated the essay needed to be 1,000 words long. That reminded me of the saying, 'a picture is worth a thousand words.' I decided to turn that phrase around. I used my 1,000 words to paint a picture."

The judges all agree Laura more than met her goal. As one judge commented, "Laura takes the reader by the hand and brings him along for the trip. The reader sees what she sees, feels what she feels, and hears and smells what she hears and smells. The setting was perfect. Who wouldn't want to visit our nation's capital? After reading Laura Cole's essay, I felt like I had experienced the outing, too. I could tell from the essay that the writer must really enjoy writing. I looked forward to meeting her."

Along with a plaque, the contest winner receives a $1,000 savings bond. But Laura says the best prize she won will be having her essay printed in the local newspaper. "I know the school board is thinking about dropping this school trip. But I could not have written my essay without that trip," she said. "We can read about Washington, D.C., in our textbooks. They can tell us about the city's history and show us photographs of the sites. However, now I know things I could only learn from being there. I know how soft the cherry blossom petals are. I can describe what they feel like. I know the sweet scent of the flowers. I know how small I felt standing next to Lincoln's feet at the monument. I could only learn those things by experiencing them."

"Fourth-Grader Wins Award" Questions

Name:_____

Directions: Circle the letter of the correct answer for each question.

1 Why were people surprised when Laura won?

a) Her essay was poorly written.

b) Laura did not follow the rules.

c) They thought an older student would win.

d) Many students wrote about the same topic.

2 Why did the judge think the setting was perfect?

a) There are many things to see, hear, smell, and touch there.

b) Laura could get the information she needed from her books.

c) Everyone has visited Washington, D.C., at least once.

d) People around the world need to know about the city.

3 Why did it take weeks to read the essays and stories?

a) Some of them were very long.

b) There were so many to read.

c) The judges visited all of the places in the essays.

d) The judges first met with all of the student writers.

4 Why is Laura happy her essay will be in the paper?

a) She has always wanted to be a famous author.

b) She wants people to learn about the monuments.

c) She wants to prove you can be a winner at any age.

d) She thinks it will show it is important to keep the school trip.

5 With which statement would Laura most likely agree?

a) The right words can change the way people think.

b) Pictures can take the place of personal experience.

c) There is no way to fairly judge writing.

d) Most contests have too many rules.

6 When did Laura visit Washington, D.C., on the school trip?

a) spring

b) when she was young

c) yesterday

d) fall

THE DAILY NEWS

_____

_____

_____

By:_____

_____

_____

_____

_____

_____

_____

_____

_____

_____

_____

_____

_____

_____

_____

_____

_____

_____

_____

_____